Improve your scales!

Paul Harris

FABER *ff* MUSIC

A♭ major

March 4th

Fill in the notes of the scale and circle the notes of the arpeggio:

Write the key signature of A♭ major:

Finger fitness

These exercises help you to practise putting your fingers down precisely. The first exercise is for intonation so listen carefully to make sure you are playing in tune.

TOP TIP There are no open strings in this scale. The 4th finger is in the same place on all strings; remember the semitones are between C–D♭ and G–A♭.

Have a go Compose or improvise your own tune in A♭ major, beginning with the following:

Amiable aria   Scale study

A tanker at anchor at Ankara   Arpeggio study

Sight-reading

1 How many repeated patterns can you find?

2 Set a pulse going and then hear the piece in your head.

3 How will you put character into your performance?

Now: **say, hear, think** and **play** the scale and arpeggio with confidence!

B major

Fill in the notes of the scale and circle the notes of the arpeggio:

Write the key signature of B major:

Finger fitness

> **TOP TIP** Remember you can't use open G, D or A strings in this key: they are all sharps, so your 4th finger will have to be a semitone higher on the G and D strings.

1

2

3

4

5

6

Have a go Compose or improvise your own tune in B major, beginning with the following:

1

Badinerie   Scale study

2

Brighton Beach   Arpeggio study

3

Sight-reading

1 Can you spot any repeated patterns?

2 Tap the pulse with one hand and the rhythm with the other.

3 Play the first note, then hear the piece in your head.

4

Now: **say, hear, think** and **play** the scale and arpeggio with confidence!

C major

Fill in the notes of the scale and circle the notes of the arpeggio:

Write the key signature of C major:

Finger fitness

> **TOP TIP** Add your own fingering to these exercises: if you are using 2nd position for the scale, you will need to play *Finger fitness* in 2nd position too.

1

2

3

4

5

6

> **Have a go** Compose or improvise your own tune in C major, beginning with the following:
>
>

Counting calories   Scale study

Crumbly cookies   Arpeggio study

Sight-reading

1 Play the scale *mf* and gracefully.

2 Do any bars have the same rhythm?

3 Play the first note then imagine yourself playing the piece, with the dynamics and bowing.

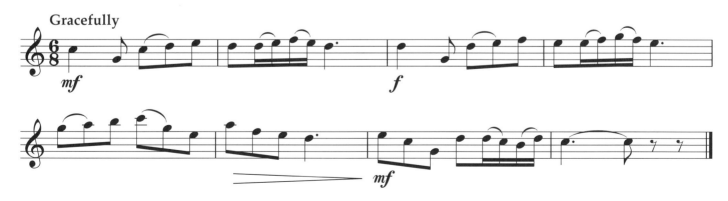

Now: **say, hear, think** and **play** the scale and arpeggio with confidence!

E major

Fill in the notes of the scale and circle the notes of the arpeggio:

Write the key signature of E major:

Finger fitness

> **TOP TIP** If you start this scale on a 2nd finger on the G string, play these exercises in 4th position. If you start in 1st position then shift, write your fingering in.

1

2

3

4

5

6

Have a go Compose or improvise your own tune in E major, beginning with the following:

Emerald   Scale study

Espresso   Arpeggio study

Sight-reading

1 Where will you shift?

2 How will you put character into your performance?

3 Play the first note, then hear the piece in your head.

Now: **say, hear, think** and **play** the scale and arpeggio with confidence!

G minor

Fill in the notes of the scale and circle the notes of the arpeggio:

☐ **Harmonic:**

☐ **Melodic:**

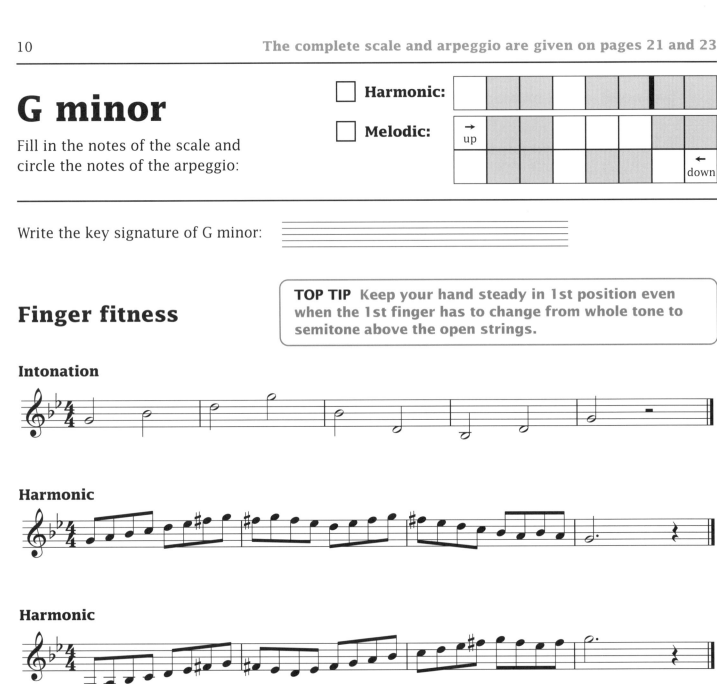

Write the key signature of G minor:

Finger fitness

> **TOP TIP** Keep your hand steady in 1st position even when the 1st finger has to change from whole tone to semitone above the open strings.

Intonation

Harmonic

Harmonic

Melodic

Melodic

Arpeggio

1

Gadzooks! Harmonic minor scale study

2

Gherkin gateau Melodic minor scale study

3

Groovy Arpeggio study

1

Have a go Compose or improvise your own tune in G minor, beginning with the following:

2

Sight-reading

1 What is the character of this piece?

2 Play the harmonic minor scale *forte*, and the arpeggio *mezzo forte*.

3 Play the first note and hear the piece in your head, including expression.

3

Sight-reading

1 Are there any similarities between the two four-bar phrases?

2 Tap the pulse with one hand and the rhythm with the other.

3 Play the first note and hear the piece in your head.

4

Now: **say, hear, think** and **play** the scale and arpeggio with confidence!

Paul Harris' Exam Workout

IMPROVE YOUR SIGHT-READING! - New Editions

The ability to sight-read fluently is an important part of musical training, whether intending to play professionally, or simply for enjoyment. By becoming a good sight-reader, the player will be able to learn pieces more quickly, pianists will accompany more easily and all musicians will play duets and chamber music with confidence and assurance. Also, in grade examinations, a good performance in the sight-reading test will result in useful extra marks!

These completely new editions are designed to help incorporate sight-reading regularly into practice and lessons, and to prepare for the sight-reading test in grade examinations. They offer a progressive series of enjoyable and stimulating stages which, with careful work, should result in considerable improvement from week to week.

Step by step, the player is encouraged to build up a complete picture of each piece. Rhythmic exercises help develop and maintain a steady beat, whilst melodic exercises assist in the recognition of melodic shapes at a glance. The study of a prepared piece with associated questions for the student to answer helps consolidate acquired skills and, finally, a series of real, unprepared sight-reading tests in *Going Solo*.

Such practical and methodical material is guaranteed to take the horror out of sight-reading!

0-571-53300-0	Piano Pre-Grade 1
0-571-53301-9	Piano Grade 1
0-571-53302-7	Piano Grade 2
0-571-53303-5	Piano Grade 3
0-571-53304-3	Piano Grade 4
0-571-53305-1	Piano Grade 5
0-571-53306-X	Piano Grade 6
0-571-53307-8	Piano Grade 7
0-571-53308-6	Piano Grade 8
0-571-53621-2	Violin Grade 1
0-571-53622-0	Violin Grade 2
0-571-53623-9	Violin Grade 3
0-571-53624-7	Violin Grade 4
0-571-53625-5	Violin Grade 5
0-571-53626-3	Violin Grade 6
0-571-53627-1	Violin Grades 7–8
0-571-53699-9	Viola Grades 1–5

0-571-53697-2	Cello Grades 1–3
0-571-53698-0	Cello Grades 4–5
0-571-53700-6	Double Bass Grades 1–5
0-571-51373-5	Descant Recorder Grades 1–3
0-571-51466-9	Flute Grades 1–3
0-571-51467-7	Flute Grades 4–5
0-571-51789-7	Flute Grade 6
0-571-51790-0	Flute Grades 7–8
0-571-51464-2	Clarinet Grades 1–3
0-571-51465-0	Clarinet Grades 4–5
0-571-51787-0	Clarinet Grade 6
0-571-51788-9	Clarinet Grades 7–8
0-571-51635-1	Saxophone Grades 1–3
0-571-51636-X	Saxophone Grades 4–5
0-571-51633-5	Oboe Grades 1–3
0-571-57021-6	Oboe Grades 4–5
0-571-51148-1	Bassoon Grades 1–5
0-571-51076-0	Horn Grades 1–5
0-571-50989-4	Trumpet Grades 1–5
0-571-51152-X	Trumpet Grades 5–8
0-571-56860-2	Trombone Grades 1–5

IMPROVE YOUR AURAL! - New Editions

The very thought of aural, especially in examinations, strikes fear into the heart of many young pianists and instrumentalists. But aural should not be an occasional optional extra – it's something to be developing all the time, because having a good ear will help improve musicianship more than any other single musical skill.

Improve your aural! is designed to take the fear out of aural. Through fun listening activities, boxes to fill in and practice exercises, these workbooks and CDs focus on all the elements of the ABRSM aural tests. Because all aspects of musical training are of course connected, the student will also be singing, clapping, playing their instrument, writing music down, improvising and composing – as well as developing that vital ability to do well at the aural test in grade exams!

0-571-53438-4	Grade 1 (with CD)
0-571-53439-2	Grade 2 (with CD)
0-571-53544-5	Grade 3 (with CD)
0-571-53545-3	Grade 4 (with CD)
0-571-53546-1	Grade 5 (with CD)
0-571-53440-6	Grade 6 (with CD)
0-571-53441-4	Grades 7–8 (with CD)

IMPROVE YOUR PRACTICE!

Improve your practice! is the essential companion for pianists and instrumentalists, encapsulating Paul Harris's failsafe approach to learning. With boxes for filling in, make-your-own playing cards, a handy practice diary and an exam countdown, these books help to explore pieces and to understand their character. The books will enable the student to develop ways of getting the most out of their practice sessions – whatever their length. Most importantly, the wider musical skills such as aural, theory, sight-reading, improvisation and composition develop alongside, resulting in a more intelligent and all-round musician. Practice makes perfect!

0-571-52844-9 Piano Beginners
0-571-52261-0 Piano Grade 1
0-571-52262-9 Piano Grade 2
0-571-52263-7 Piano Grade 3
0-571-52264-5 Piano Grade 4
0-571-52265-3 Piano Grade 5

0-571-52271-8 Instrumental Grade 1
0-571-52272-6 Instrumental Grade 2
0-571-52273-4 Instrumental Grade 3
0-571-52274-2 Instrumental Grade 4
0-571-52275-0 Instrumental Grade 5

IMPROVE YOUR TEACHING!

Energising and inspirational, *Improve your teaching!* and *Teaching Beginners* are 'must have' handbooks for all instrumental and singing teachers. Packed full of comprehensive advice and practical strategies, they offer creative yet accessible solutions to the challenges faced in music education.
These insightful volumes are distilled from years of personal experience and research. In his approachable style, Paul Harris outlines his innovative strategy of 'simultaneous learning' as well as offering advice on lesson preparation, aural and memory work, effective practice and more.

0-571-52534-2 Improve your teaching!
0-571-53175-X Improve your teaching! Teaching beginners
0-571-53319-1 Group Music Teaching in Practice (with ECD)

THE VIRTUOSO TEACHER

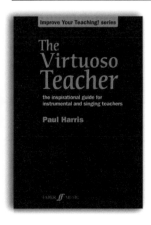

By considering **The Virtuoso Teacher** and how a teacher might attain virtuoso status, renowned educator and writer Paul Harris delves into the core issues of being a teacher and the teaching process. A fascinating look at topics such as self-awareness and the importance of emotional intelligence; getting the best out of pupils; dealing with challenging pupils; asking the right questions; creating a master-plan; taking the stress out of learning and teaching for the right reasons. This seminal book is an inspirational read for all music teachers, encouraging everyone to consider themselves in a new and uplifted light, and transform their teaching.

0-571-53676-X   The Virtuoso Teacher

IMPROVE YOUR SCALES!

Paul Harris's *Improve your scales!* series is the only way to learn scales.

These workbooks contains not only the complete scales and arpeggios for the current ABRSM syllabuses but also use finger fitness exercises, scale and arpeggio studies, key pieces and simple improvisations to help you play scales and arpeggios with real confidence.

This unique approach encourages the student to understand and play comfortably within in a key, thus helping them pick up those valuable extra marks in exams, as well as promoting a solid basis for the learning of repertoire and for sight-reading.

0-571-53411-2	Piano Grade 1
0-571-53412-0	Piano Grade 2
0-571-53413-9	Piano Grade 3
0-571-53414-7	Piano Grade 4
0-571-53415-5	Piano Grade 5
0-571-53701-4	Violin Grade 1
0-571-53702-2	Violin Grade 2
0-571-53703-0	Violin Grade 3
0-571-53704-9	Violin Grade 4
0-571-53705-7	Violin Grade 5
0-571-52024-3	Flute Grades 1–3
0-571-52025-1	Flute Grades 4–5
0-571-51475-8	Clarinet Grades 1–3
0-571-51476-6	Clarinet Grades 4–5

Contact us:

Faber Music Ltd.
Burnt Mill
Elizabeth Way
Harlow
Essex
CM20 2HX

t: +44 (0)1279 828982
f: +44 (0)1279 828983
e: sales@fabermusic.com
w: www.fabermusicstore.com
 @fabermusic
facebook.com/fabermusic

FABER *ff* MUSIC

B minor

Fill in the notes of the scale and
circle the notes of the arpeggio:

☐ **Harmonic:**

☐ **Melodic:**

Write the key signature of B minor:

Finger fitness

> **TOP TIP** Remember you have the choice of playing
> harmonic or melodic minor, but notes from either scale
> can be used in pieces, so try to understand both.

Intonation

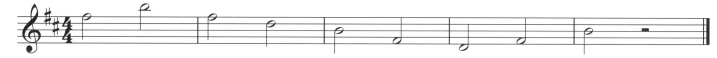

Harmonic

Harmonic

Melodic

Melodic

Arpeggio

1

Blackberry bush   Harmonic minor scale study

2

Buccaneer   Melodic minor scale study

3

Burly butcher   Arpeggio study

Have a go Compose or improvise your own tune in B minor, beginning with the following:

Sight-reading

1 How often does the rhythm pattern in bars 1–2 repeat?
2 Play the appropriate scale including the various dynamic levels in the piece.
3 Play the first note and hear the piece in your head, including expression and dynamic levels.

Sight-reading

1 Which version of this scale is used here? Play it, including dynamics from the piece.
2 Tap the pulse with one hand and the rhythm with the other.
3 Play the first note then hear the piece in your head, imagining the fingering.

Now: **say, hear, think** and **play** the scale and arpeggio with confidence!

C minor

Fill in the notes of the scale and
circle the notes of the arpeggio:

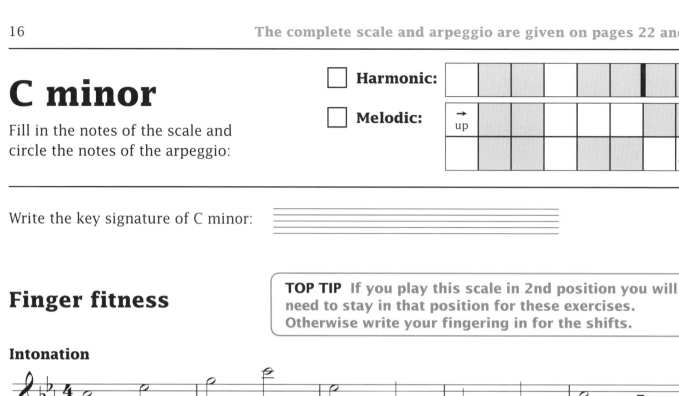

☐ **Harmonic:**

☐ **Melodic:**

Write the key signature of C minor:

Finger fitness

> **TOP TIP** If you play this scale in 2nd position you will
> need to stay in that position for these exercises.
> Otherwise write your fingering in for the shifts.

Intonation

1 ☐

Harmonic

2 ☐

Harmonic

3 ☐

Melodic

4 ☐

Melodic

5 ☐

Arpeggio

6 ☐

1 Creepy crawly   Harmonic minor scale study

Andante misterioso

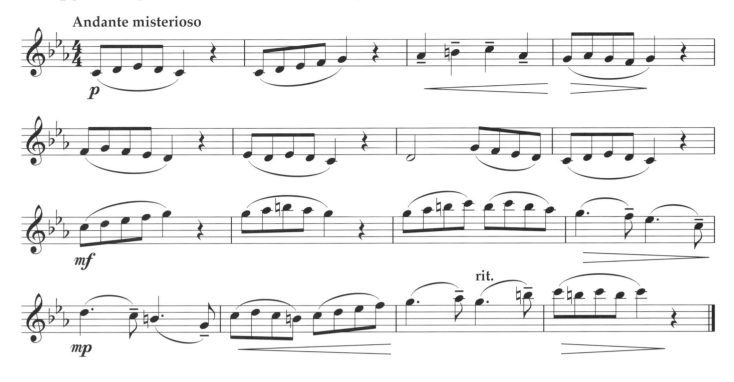

2 Cruising on the Clyde   Melodic minor scale study

Con moto

3 Carnival caprice   Arpeggio study

Allegro spiritoso

1

Have a go Compose or improvise your own tune in C minor, beginning with the following:

2

Sight-reading

1 How do bars 1–2 differ from bars 5–6?

2 Play the scale, including various dynamics from the piece.

3 Play the first note and hear the piece in your head, including expression.

3

Sight-reading

1 Which version of the scale does this use? Play it, including dynamics from the piece.

2 Does the rhythm of the opening bar return?

3 Play the first note and hear the piece in your head.

4

Now: **say, hear, think** and **play** the scale and arpeggio with confidence!

Chromatics

Chromatic scales go up in **semitone steps**, meaning you play all the notes, and your fingers are always next to each other. You will need to slide your fingers up between some notes or you will run out of fingers!

> **TOP TIP** Keep your arm and hand in first position all the time, and slide your fingers lightly on the string where necessary between notes.

Finger fitness

1 | Antelope   Chromatic study on A

2 | Exciting event   Chromatic study on E

Dominant seventh studies

A dominant seventh is a pattern which is built on the dominant (5th note) of the key.
It is made up of four notes: the first, third, fifth and minor seventh above the dominant.

> **TOP TIP** There is a semitone change for the second
> finger (*Curves and corners*) or third finger (*Dizzy*) as it
> crosses the string from major third to minor 7th above
> the dominant root.

1

Curves and corners   Dominant 7th study in C major

2

Dizzy   Dominant 7th study in D major

Complete
Grade 4 scales

Long tonic
The even note rhythm is available to download from Fabermusic.com

Exam requirements of the Associated Board:

Scales:
- A♭, B, C, E majors and G, B, C harmonic or melodic minors (2 octaves)
- Separate bows **and** slurred (2 beats to a bow)
- Long tonic **or** even notes (even notes available to download)
- Chromatic on A and E, separate bows **and** slurred (4 beats to a bow)
- For Grade 4 exams, the minimum tempo for scales is ♩ = 69.

☐ **A♭ major**

☐ **B major**

☐ **C major**

☐ **E major**

☐ **G harmonic minor**

☐ **G melodic minor**

B harmonic minor

B melodic minor

C harmonic minor

C melodic minor

Chromatic on A

Chromatic on E

Complete
Grade 4 arpeggios

For Grade 4 exams, the minimum tempo for arpeggios is ♩ = 40.

Arpeggios:
- A♭, B, C, E majors and G, B, C minors (2 octaves)
- Separate bows **and** slurred (3 notes to a bow)
- Dominant sevenths in the key of C and D (separate bows only)

Practice chart

Practise your scales and arpeggios in different ways – with different rhythms
and dynamics and perhaps thinking of different colours and flavours!

Scale/Arpeggio	Comments	Tick a box each time you practise														
A♭ major scale																
A♭ major arpeggio																
B major scale																
B major arpeggio																
C major scale																
C major arpeggio																
E major scale																
E major arpeggio																
G minor scale	Harmonic or melodic															
G minor arpeggio																
B minor scale	Harmonic or melodic															
B minor arpeggio																
C minor scale	Harmonic or melodic															
C minor arpeggio																
Chromatic on A																
Chromatic on E																
Dominant seventh in C																
Dominant seventh in D																

With many thanks to Gillian Secret for her invaluable help.

© 2012 Faber Music Ltd
First published in 2012 by Faber Music Ltd
Bloomsbury House 74–77 Great Russell Street London WC1B 3DA
Music processed by Donald Thomson
Cover and text designed by Susan Clarke
Printed in England by Caligraving Ltd

ISBN10: 0-571-53704-9
EAN13: 978-0-571-53704-4

To buy Faber Music Publications or to find out about the full range of titles
available please contact your local music retailer or Faber Music sales enquiries:

Faber Music Ltd, Burnt Mill, Elizabeth Way, Harlow CM20 2HX
Tel: +44(0) 1279 82 89 82   Fax: +44(0) 1279 82 89 83
sales@fabermusic.com   fabermusic.com